The LADYBIRD book of RHYMES

by DOROTHY *and* JOHN TAYLOR
with illustrations by
BRIAN PRICE THOMAS

Ladybird Books Loughborough 1977

Round and round the garden
Like a teddy bear;
One step, two step,
Tickle you under there.

2

This little pig went to market,
This little pig stayed at home,
This little pig had roast beef,
This little pig had none,
And this little pig cried:
Wee-wee-wee,
I can't find my way home.

5

There were two blackbirds
Sitting on a hill,
The one named Jack,
The other named Jill.

Fly away, Jack!
Fly away, Jill!
Come again, Jack!
Come again, Jill!

Pat-a-cake, pat-a-cake,
Baker's man,
Bake me a cake
As fast as you can.
Pat it and prick it
And mark it with 'B'
And put it in the oven
For Baby and me.

Incy wincy spider,
Climbing up the spout,
Down came the rain,
And washed the spider out.

Out came the sunshine,
Dried up all the rain,
Incy wincy spider,
Climbed the spout again.

Five currant buns in a baker's shop,
Round and fat with sugar on the top.
Along came a boy with a penny one day,
Bought a currant bun and took it away.

13

My mother said that if I should
Play with the gipsies in the wood,
She would say, 'You naughty girl!
You naughty girl to disobey!'

14

One, two, kittens that mew,
Two, three, birds on a tree,
Three, four, shells on the shore,
Four, five, bees from the hive,
Five, six, the cow that licks,
Six, seven, rooks in the heaven,
Seven, eight, sheep at the gate,
Eight, nine, clothes on a line,
Nine, ten, the little black hen.

1, 2,
Buckle
my
shoe;

3, 4,
Knock
at the door;

5, 6,
Pick up sticks;

7, 8,
Lay them
straight;

9, 10,
A big fat hen;

11, 12,
Dig and delve;

13, 14,
Maids a-courting;

15, 16,
Maids in the kitchen;

17, 18,
Maids in waiting;

19, 20,
My plate's empty.

One I love, two I love,
Three I love, I say:
Four I love with all my heart,
Five I cast away.
Six he loves, seven she loves,
Eight they love together;
Nine he comes, ten he tarries,
Eleven he woos, and twelve he marries.

Seven black friars, sitting back to back,
Fished from the bridge for a pike or a jack.
The first caught a tiddler,
The second caught a crab,
The third caught a winkle,
The fourth caught a dab,
The fifth caught a tadpole,
The sixth caught an eel,
The seventh one caught an old cart-wheel.

Knock, knock, knock, knock –
Hear the knockings four!
Each a knock for someone standing
At our kitchen door.

The first is a beggar man,
The second is a thief,
The third is a pirate,
And the fourth a robber chief.

Close all the windows,
Lock the door, and then
Call for the policeman quick
To catch those four bad men!

There were two wrens upon a tree,
Whistle and I'll come to thee,
Another came and there were three,
Whistle and I'll come to thee;
Another came, and there were four,
You needn't whistle any more,
For being frightened, off they flew,
And there are none to show to you.

Bell horses, bell horses,
What time of day?
One o'clock, two o'clock,
Three and away.

Bell horses, bell horses,
What time of day?
Two o'clock, three o'clock,
Four and away.

Bell horses, bell horses,
What time of day?
Five o'clock, six o'clock,
Now time to stay.

Bell hor - ses, bell hor - ses, What time of day? One o'clock, two o'clock, Three and a - way.

One, two, three, four, five,
Once I caught a fish alive.
Six, seven, eight, nine, ten,
Then I let it go again.

Why did you let it go?
Because it bit my finger so.
Which finger did it bite?
This little finger on the right.

One man went to mow,
Went to mow a meadow,
One man and his dog,
Went to mow a meadow.

Two men went to mow,
Went to mow a meadow,
Two men, one man and his dog,
Went to mow a meadow.

Three men went to mow,

Four men went to mow,

Five men, *etc*.

One man went to mow, Went to mow a mea-dow,
One man and his dog, Went to mow a mea-dow.

The first day of Christmas,
My true love sent to me:
A partridge in a pear tree.

The second day of Christmas,
My true love sent to me:
Two turtle doves and
A partridge in a pear tree.

The third day of Christmas,
My true love sent to me:
Three French hens, two turtle doves and
A partridge in a pear tree.

The fourth day of Christmas,
My true love sent to me:
Four colly birds, three French hens,
Two turtle doves and
A partridge in a pear tree.

The fifth day of Christmas,
My true love sent to me:
Five gold rings, four colly birds,
Three French hens, two turtle doves and
A partridge in a pear tree.

The sixth day of Christmas . . .
Six geese a-laying, *five gold rings, etc.*

The seventh day of Christmas . . .
Seven swans a-swimming, *six geese a-laying, etc.*

The eighth day of Christmas . . .
Eight maids a-milking, *seven swans a-swimming, etc.*

The ninth day of Christmas . . .
Nine drummers drumming, *eight maids a-milking, etc.*

The tenth day of Christmas . . .
Ten pipers piping, *nine drummers drumming, etc.*

The eleventh day of Christmas . . .
Eleven ladies dancing, *ten pipers piping, etc.*

The twelfth day of Christmas . . .
Twelve lords a-leaping, *eleven ladies dancing, etc.*

The first day of Christmas, my true love sent to me: a part-ridge in a pear tree.

The se-cond day of Christmas, my true love sent to me: two tur-tle doves and a part-ridge in a pear tree.

The third day of Christmas, my true love sent to me: three French hens, two turtle doves and a part-ridge in a pear tree.

The fourth day of Christmas, my true love sent to me: four col-ly birds, three French hens, two tur-tle doves and a part-ridge in a pear tree.

The fifth day of Christmas, my true love sent to me: five gold-rings, four col-ly birds, three French hens, two tur-tle doves and a part-ridge in a pear tree.

verses 6-12

The sixth day of Christmas, my
seventh
etc.

true love sent to me six geese a-lay-ing, five gold— rings, four col-ly birds,
seven
etc.

three French hens, two tur-tle doves and a part-ridge in a pear tree. The

38

The cuckoo

In April,
Come he will.
In May,
Sing all day.
In June,
Change his tune.
In July,
Prepare to fly.
In August,
Go he must!

41

February

*April June
September November*

*January March May
July August October
December*

Thirty days hath September,
April, June and November;
All the rest have thirty one,
Excepting February alone,
And that has twenty eight days clear
And twenty nine in each leap year.

42

Monday's child is fair of face,
Tuesday's child is full of grace,
Wednesday's child is full of woe,
Thursday's child has far to go,
Friday's child is loving and giving,
Saturday's child works hard for a living,
And the child that is born on the Sabbath day
Is bonny and blithe, and good and gay.

A was an Apple pie, B Bit it, C Cut it,
D Dealt it, E Eat it, F Fought for it,
G Got it, H Had it, I Inspected it,
J Joined for it, K Kept it, L Longed for it,
M Mourned for it, N Nodded at it,
O Opened it, P Peeped in it,
Q Quartered it, R Ran for it, S Stole it,
T Took it, U Upset it, V Viewed it,
W Wanted it,
XYZ All wished for a piece in hand.

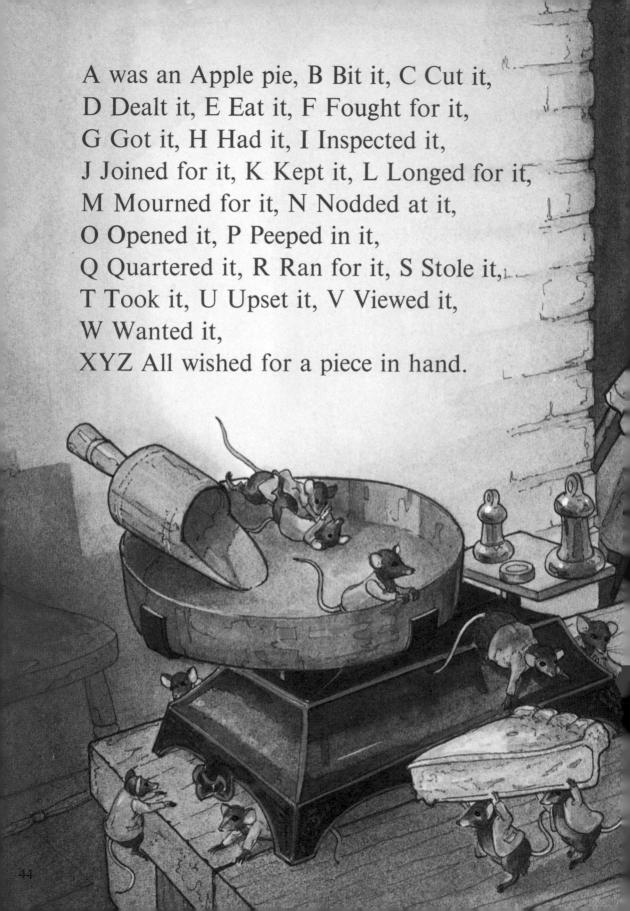

Great A was alarmed at B's bad behaviour,
Because C, D, E, F, denied G a favour,
H had a husband with I, J, K, and L,
M married Mary and taught her scholars how to spell;
A, B, C, D, E, F, G, H, I, J, K, L, M, N,
O, P, Q, R, S, T, U, V, W, X, Y, Z.

CDEFG

IJKL

M ABC

Solomon Grundy,
Born on a Monday,
Christened on Tuesday,
Married on Wednesday,
Took ill on Thursday,
Worse on Friday,
Died on Saturday,
Buried on Sunday.
This is the end
Of Solomon Grundy.

A, B, C, D, E, F, G,
Little Robin Redbreast sitting on a tree;
H, I, J, K, L, M, N,
He made love to little Jenny Wren;
O, P, Q, R, S, T, U,
Dear little Jenny, I want to marry you.
V, W, X, Y, Z,
Poor little Jenny she blushed quite red.

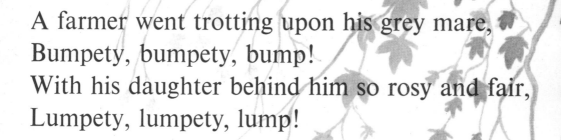

A farmer went trotting upon his grey mare,
Bumpety, bumpety, bump!
With his daughter behind him so rosy and fair,
Lumpety, lumpety, lump!

A raven cried, 'Croak!'
And they all tumbled down,
Bumpety, bumpety, bump!
The mare broke her knees
And the farmer his crown,
Lumpety, lumpety, lump!

The mischievous raven
Flew laughing away,
Bumpety, bumpety, bump!
And vowed he would serve them
The same the next day,
Lumpety, lumpety, lump!

Anna Elise, she jumped with surprise;
The surprise was so quick, it played her a trick;
The trick was so rare, she jumped in a chair;
The chair was so frail, she jumped in a pail;
The pail was so wet, she jumped in a net;
The net was so small, she jumped on the ball;
The ball was so round, she jumped on the ground;
And ever since then she's been turning around.

My dame hath a lame tame crane,
My dame hath a crane that is lame.
Pray, gentle Jane, let my dame's lame tame crane
Feed and come home again.

This rhyme can be sung as a 'round'—a piece of music repeated by one or more voices, each entering before the previous voice has finished to produce an overlapping effect.

When the first voice reaches 2 a new voice enters singing the first line. When the latter reaches 2 another voice can enter singing the first line, and so on. The round can then be repeated at will.

My dame hath a lame tame crane,   My dame hath a crane that is lame.

Pray, gentle Jane, let my dame's lame tame crane Feed and come home a - gain.

Hoddley, poddley, puddle and fogs,
Cats are to marry the poodle dogs;
Cats in blue jackets, and dogs in red hats,
What will become of the mice and rats?

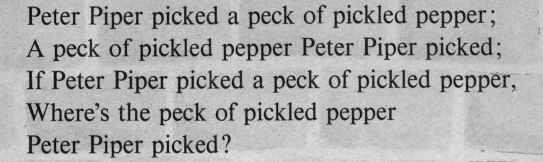

Peter Piper picked a peck of pickled pepper;
A peck of pickled pepper Peter Piper picked;
If Peter Piper picked a peck of pickled pepper,
Where's the peck of pickled pepper
Peter Piper picked?

Higglety, pigglety, pop!
The dog has eaten the mop;
The pig's in a hurry,
The cat's in a flurry,
Higglety, pigglety, pop!

Thomas a Tattamus took two T's
To tie two tups to two tall trees.
To frighten the terrible Thomas a Tattamus
Tell me how many T's there are in all that.

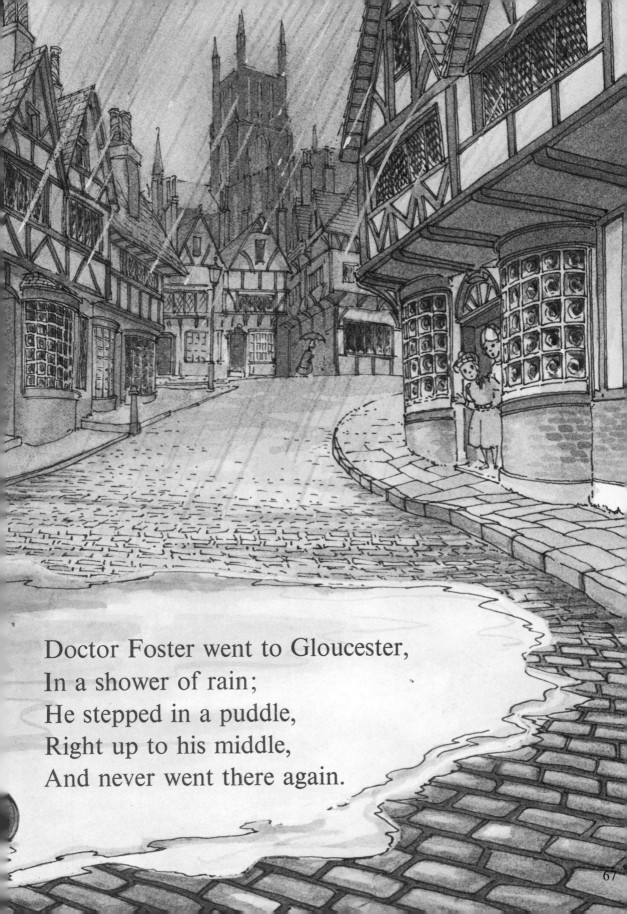

Doctor Foster went to Gloucester,
In a shower of rain;
He stepped in a puddle,
Right up to his middle,
And never went there again.

The old woman must stand
At the tub, tub, tub,
The dirty clothes
To rub, rub, rub;
But when they are clean,
And fit to be seen,
She'll dress like a lady,
And dance on the green.

There was a man lived in the moon

There was a man lived in the moon,
Lived in the moon, lived in the moon,
There was a man lived in the moon,
And his name was Aiken Drum.

And he played upon a ladle,
A ladle, a ladle,
And he played upon a ladle,
And his name was Aiken Drum.

And his hat was made of good cream cheese,
Of good cream cheese, of good cream cheese,
And his hat was made of good cream cheese,
And his name was Aiken Drum.

And he played upon a ladle, etc.

And his coat was made of good roast beef, *etc.*

And his buttons were made of penny loaves, *etc.*

And his waistcoat was made of crust of pies, *etc.*

And his breeches were made of haggis bags, *etc.*

The children can mime each verse of this rhyme—Verse 1, point to sky (for moon), Verse 2, touch head (for hat), Verse 3, clutch collar (for coat), and so on, strumming as with guitar chorus.

There — was a man lived in the moon, Lived in the moon, lived

in the moon, There was a man lived in the moon, And his name was Aik - en

Drum. And he played up - on a la - dle, a la - dle, a

la - dle, And he played up - on a la - dle, And his name was Aik - en Drum.

Are you sleeping, are you sleeping,
Brother John, Brother John?
Ring the bells for matins,
Ring the bells for matins,
Ding, ding, dong.
Ding, ding, dong.

Frère Jacques, Frère Jacques,
Dormez-vous, dormez-vous?
Sonnez les matines, sonnez les matines,
Din, din, don.
Din, din, don.

*The most usual miming action performed to this rhyme
is bell-pulling.*

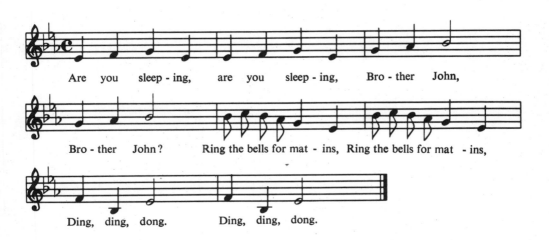

Old McDonald had a farm

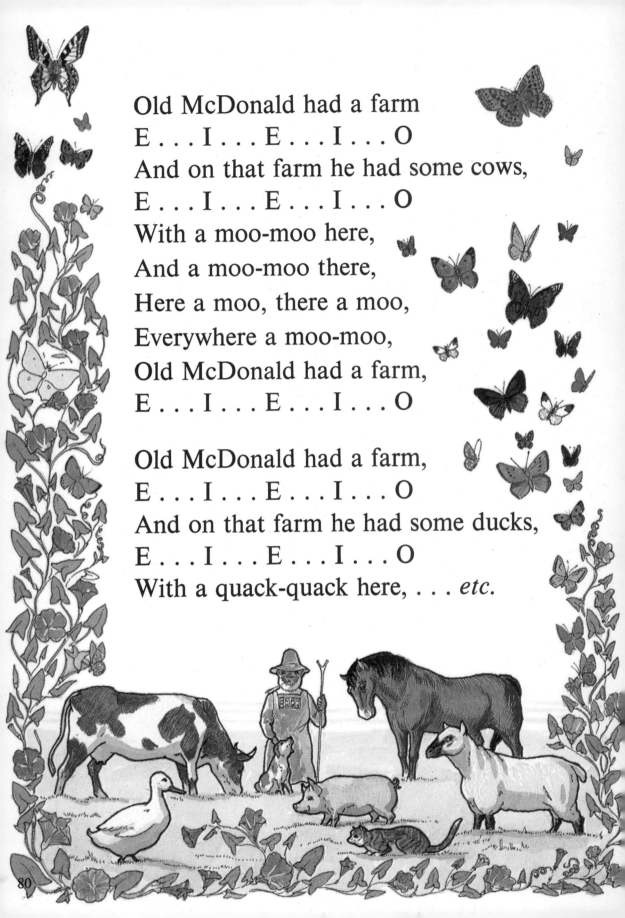

Old McDonald had a farm
E . . . I . . . E . . . I . . . O
And on that farm he had some cows,
E . . . I . . . E . . . I . . . O
With a moo-moo here,
And a moo-moo there,
Here a moo, there a moo,
Everywhere a moo-moo,
Old McDonald had a farm,
E . . . I . . . E . . . I . . . O

Old McDonald had a farm,
E . . . I . . . E . . . I . . . O
And on that farm he had some ducks,
E . . . I . . . E . . . I . . . O
With a quack-quack here, . . . *etc.*

. . . cats . . . mew-mew . . .

. . . horses . . . neigh-neigh . . .

. . . dogs . . . woof-woof . . .

. . . lambs . . . baa-baa . . .

Adjust the speed of this song to suit the age of the child; older children can be encouraged to memorise what has gone before

e.g. 'with a quack-quack here,
And a quack-quack there,
Here a quack, there a quack,
Everywhere a quack-quack,
Moo-moo-here, moo-moo-there, etc.

Old Mc - Don - ald had a farm, E - I - E - I - O —And

on that farm he had some cows, E - I - E - I - O —With a

moo - moo here, And a moo - moo there, Here a moo, there a moo, Ev'rywhere a moo-moo.

Old Mc - Don - ald had a farm, E - I - E - I - O —

Sing a song of sixpence,
A pocket full of rye;
Four and twenty blackbirds
Baked in a pie!
When the pie was opened
The birds began to sing;
Wasn't that a dainty dish
To set before the king?

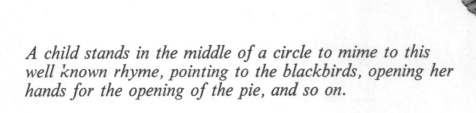

*A child stands in the middle of a circle to mime to this
well known rhyme, pointing to the blackbirds, opening her
hands for the opening of the pie, and so on.*

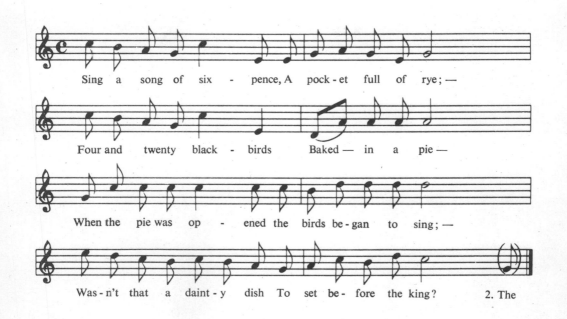

Sing a song of six - pence, A pock-et full of rye; —

Four and twenty black - birds Baked — in a pie —

When the pie was op - ened the birds be-gan to sing; —

Was-n't that a daint-y dish To set be-fore the king?   2. The

The king was in his counting house,
Counting out his money;

The queen was in the parlour,
Eating bread and honey.

The maid was in the garden,
Hanging out the clothes,

When down came a blackbird
And pecked off her nose.

I had a little nut-tree,
Nothing would it bear
But a silver nutmeg
And a golden pear;
The King of Spain's daughter
Came to visit me,
And all for the sake of my little nut-tree.
I skipped over water,
I danced over sea,
And all the birds in the air couldn't catch me.

O, have you seen the muffin man,
The muffin man, the muffin man;
O, have you seen the muffin man
Who lives in Drury Lane O?

O yes, I've seen the muffin man,
The muffin man, the muffin man;
O yes, I've seen the muffin man
Who lives in Drury Lane O.

*Players join hands to form a ring.
One child is blindfolded and stands
in the centre with a stick or rolled
newspaper in his hand.*

*Everyone sings the QUESTION verse.
At the end the blindfolded player touches
someone in the ring. This person sings
the RESPONSE verse at the end of which
the blindfolded child guesses who it can be.*

*If correct, the two children change places and
the game can begin again.*

O, have you seen the muf-fin man, The muf-fin man, the muf-fin man; O,
have you seen the muf-fin man Who lives in Dru-ry Lane O?